Hare's Journey of a Thousand Miles

Lorraine Stamp

With happiness and smiles
enjoy the story

with love
Lorraine
Brant
X

ISBN 978 – 139993326 – 1

Printed and bound by the Somerton printery Ltd. Tel: 01458 272368
www.somertonprintery.com

Foreword

I first met Lorraine when she became a student of mine on the Neuroscience Professional Development Programme.

She was hungry to learn as much as she could about why people do what they do. Lorraine went on to join our Learning Lab, a deeper dive into neuroscience, whilst at the same time studying for a master's degree in Positive Psychology.

Why is this important? Because she strives for self-improvement so that she can help others as well. She is a person of integrity and is generous of spirit. And this book, *Hare's Journey of a Thousand Miles,* is testimony to her gentle and determined nature.

In short, you are about to read a fable that we can all relate to. As the words unfold, I wager that you will feel what it is like to be Hare, and the primary message will become clear to the point of real understanding, like a realisation that is relevant to you, no matter where you are at the moment.

I thoroughly enjoyed this delightful read, in fact I read it twice and saw something different the second time. Perhaps I will continue to revisit it from time to time.

Thank you, Lorraine.

Dr Lynda Shaw
Neuroscientist and Author of Your Brain Is Boss

This book has been written for you. Yes you, the one who has chosen to read this, so thank you. My hope is that it inspires you in your own life to make the right choices for YOU!

A huge thank you for this book to be born goes to Rowen Campbell, you truly are one inspirational lady, and I am blessed that we came together on one of my programmes.

I would also like to thank my family and friends who have been there for me over the years to live a much healthier and happier life. I would add that some of you have also taught me some of the biggest lessons in life so far.

There are so many people that have inspired me in my life. You know who you are. Thank you

Thank you to all my reviewers, proof-readers, and accountability buddies. You are all so talented and helpful and I couldn't have got this far without you.

Of course, I could not go without mentioning my furry friends "Jacob, Robbie, Lady, Tramp, Yogi, Amber, Woody, Pickles, Scrappy Doo, and Poppy. 9 of you have left this physical world but you will always have a place in my heart, because you showed me the real meaning of life and what true love really is.

There is one other person who I will keep anonymous. They transformed my whole way of thinking and had so much belief in me from the day we met, you have made me whole and complete again. I love you.

Hare's Journey of a Thousand Miles

Lorraine Stamp

As she reached the top of the hill, Hare stopped. A few precious seconds to catch her breath. She looked back over her shoulder for a moment, back at everything she'd left behind, and felt a chill. It was mid-afternoon but the hillside and the woods beyond it looked almost dark.

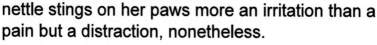

She paused, to lick her wounds; the scratches from the brambles she'd pushed through as she fought to break past the thorns, the nettle stings on her paws more an irritation than a pain but a distraction, nonetheless.

She turned her attention to her hind leg, where Snake had managed to land a bite. It was healing now but it would take time, and Hare wondered whether there would always be a scar. That would be ok, she thought. It was part of her story now. Snake was no longer in her life; she'd outrun him, and she was free to choose her own direction now. And the scar would remind her of just how far she'd come.

Hare would forgive Snake in time, but not yet. And she would not forget. Forgiving would allow her to move forwards, though if she were to forget, the lesson would be lost.

Hare allowed herself a moment to consider her thoughts and reflect.

She had been cornered for a long time while  Snake slithered around her, slowly, gradually, reducing the space Hare had until she felt completely trapped and it looked like there would only be one sad but inevitable ending.

It was suffocating.

It seemed so obvious now looking back, but in the moment, with Snake's cunning ways and clever tricks, it had been difficult for Hare to see what was happening to her.

Owl had swooped past them one day and the breeze powered by the swoosh of his wings had made Hare look up. She saw sunlight above her and watched Owl as he landed on a branch, high above everyone else in the forest, minding his own business.

He could see everything from up there and he knew exactly what was going on.

Hare watched Owl a bit longer, fascinated by his composure as he ruffled his feathers and settled into position. She thought she might like to be more like that one day.

The sound of Snake's hiss had brought her back to reality and she locked eyes with him once more.

She had more fight left in her – not much – but she was determined that this was not how her story ended.

She wanted more from her time. And she deserved it.

If you were to ask Hare now how she escaped in the end, she'd struggle to tell you. That's in part because her mind is powerful and has taken steps to block some memories as a way of protecting herself. Some memories are still raw, and she prefers to keep them buried deep inside. And partly because there is no single answer.

What she did realise was that once you know what you want, or what you don't want anymore, it is down to you alone to make it happen. By being true to herself, Hare was able to find a way.

Now, at the top of the hill, she saw the long shadow of Owl stretching in front of her, the sun behind them warming her back, and without looking up she knew once again he was in the tree above her. It was a comfort to know he was there, and she found his presence calming.

"I want to be able to fly, like you," Hare confessed, breaking the silence.

"But what on earth for?!" Owl asked, "You don't need to fly. You just need to make sure you do what you do to the best of your ability. You owe yourself that much."

Hare lowered her ears to concentrate and sank to the ground while she thought about what Owl had said. Always on her guard, defences up, perpetually ready for fight or flight, she could hear her heart thumping inside her chest.

"Slipping into water doesn't necessarily mean drowning, Hare," Owl counselled, "But the chances are much higher if you don't lift up your head."

Of course. Owl's words were the affirmation she needed to know that she was right. She didn't need all the answers now. The most important thing was believing that she herself had the power to choose her direction and which path to take next. If something changed along the way, she had the power to come back, to re-route, to carve her own path. More answers would reveal themselves along the way. She had done the hardest work in acknowledging her desire to change, and in taking the first tentative step on her journey.

Relaxing, Hare stood up and turned her focus to what was ahead of her. She looked out towards the rolling, verdant fields before her, bathed in sunshine and opportunity.

Hare had crossed many fields now and had come such a long way she could no longer see the hill she'd stopped on. More hills stood between her and where she had come from. The earth was different here, Hare noticed. It was another colour, and she didn't recognise the crop the farmer was growing. Spying a water trough in the corner of the field, she was suddenly very aware of how thirsty she had become, but also that she was alone in a strange place and taking a drink could be risky. She hopped over, looking around constantly, lest she be caught in the act of helping herself.

Peering nervously into the vessel, she studied her

reflection. It didn't look like Hare anymore. Not the Hare she remembered, anyway. This Hare was tired. Unsure. She stared, trying to recognise the face looking back at her, and as she looked deeper, she saw Snake's face appear in the dark water, alongside her own.

"Give it up, Hare. You're not all that. Look at you – who'd listen to you? Leave it to an animal that's worth something."

Snake's words kept ringing around Hare's head and even when she closed her eyes, trying to shut out the image, she could still see Snake there. She shook her head from side to side, trying to dislodge the picture inside. She was sure she could feel the pain rise once more in her leg where his fangs had punctured her skin, but when she checked, the scar was still there, the wound continuing to heal. How do you free yourself when it's your own mind holding you prisoner?

So, she ran. Her thirst pushed aside, Hare ran and ran, with no clear destination in mind, but just knowing she had to get away. Far away. She needed to be somewhere very different, and quickly. Hare left herself no time to think, hoping that by the time she stopped, her physical exhaustion would be beaten only by the exhaustion of her mind, and she might be able to stop the noise in her head.

Just as she thought her legs would carry her no further, she reached a sunny spot, surrounded by beautiful meadow flowers, and allowed herself a break. Admiring the rich scarlet of the poppies in the field around her, she heard birds singing in the hedgerow. Two dormice scampered past Hare, so caught up in themselves and their conversation that they didn't even seem to notice her. A couple of stoats followed soon after, again not appearing to notice Hare, so much so that she had to take a quick step back and pull her paws out of the way to prevent them from being stepped on. Even the butterflies were pottering about in pairs.

Being alone felt different now. There had been

a shift and Hare hadn't even notice it happen, but the solitude she once craved and relied on was much more like isolation when she looked again, and she didn't know how to get out.

Perhaps she really was invisible. Maybe Snake was right, and the animals just didn't notice her. She looked around, missing her connection with other animals, but based on all she'd heard and stored inside her head, and the evidence of the creatures just now, she would be all alone again this evening and it fell to her to find somewhere safe and dry to spend the night.

Hare had learned that being reliant only on oneself meant that the dark hours tended to yield little sleep and were instead the playground of her mind's inner prankster, sharing long-buried memories, potentially threatening sounds, and an unimaginable number of possible risks hiding in the shadows. Time always passed slower at night.

The fur bristled on the back of Hare's neck, an involuntary warning that something was amiss. She felt like she was being watched and turned slowly. Fox grinned at her.

"Afternoon!" Fox called over, "Fancy seeing you all the way out here!" Hare tried to recall the last time she'd seen Fox, but that had no importance compared to the relief of having a familiar face. Animals who knew them had often passed comment or raised an eyebrow at their friendship, and Hare had always ignored them. Fox was one of her oldest friends, but they'd not seen much of each other recently.

From the first time they'd met, Fox had been so kind. She was fun. She gave Hare gifts and made her laugh. Fox always had a colourful story to tell and Hare and others loved to listen.

Why had they lost touch? Hare racked her brains as Fox updated her on all the wonderful things, she was doing to support Rabbit, who'd fallen on hard times.

"I really am the most helpful person I know," Fox beamed as the story came to an end, "You should try it sometime." And there it was, an innocuous little sentence that brought it all back and she recalled exactly why she hadn't seen Fox in so long. The compliments that had been so plentiful to start with had gradually started to become barbed. They began to come with a sting in the tail that left Hare feeling worse.

Maybe she had imagined it – after all, there wasn't

 really anything overtly unkind in it. Perhaps she was just too sensitive. Fox had suggested that lots of times.

It had been so lovely in the beginning; they'd just clicked. Fox had made time for Hare, they'd done things together, been places, had fun. Hare had been quite happy to drop things for Fox when she'd needed Hare's support, because that's what friends do, isn't it? You're there for each other, and when the time came that Hare needed help herself, Fox would be there for her, Hare was sure of it.

Except that Fox wasn't there.

She was always busy when Hare asked for something. She told Hare her worries were silly. They weren't anything compared to what Fox was going through. What gave Hare the right to be so self-centred? And just when Hare was thinking that maybe she was being dramatic and her feelings were insignificant, Fox would arrange something lovely for them to do, together. Her idea, her terms. It all seemed well again and perhaps Hare was imagining things.

No. Hare was determined this time. She wouldn't be drawn in again. It wasn't fair that she should allow herself to be put down for Fox to make herself feel better.

"Listen Fox," Hare started, digging her claws into her own paws to make sure she concentrated and didn't give in. "It's lovely to see you. We've been such a big part of each other's lives now for so long, but I'm on a journey at the moment and I can't stop. I have to keep going, for me."

And before Fox had a chance to respond, Hare left, waving as she ran, and feeling as if she had avoided a big trap that would have been bad news for her. Her heart thumped inside her chest much more violently than from the run alone, yet still she ran.

Determination drove her on, and a want, a need, to do things differently now.

As she finally began to drop the pace, Hare spotted Owl in the next field, perched high up in the branches of an oak tree. He was watching her, silently. He caught Hare looking and held her gaze, and to Hare it was as if someone had pulled her whiskers. She felt a wave of emotion wash through her body and the connection with another being she had longed for was made. Not forced, not hurried. Owl had simply not given up. He hadn't blinked, he hadn't looked away.

"Owl doesn't need to say anything," Hare thought, as she continued to look up. "I know he supports me; I can feel it." And she could. It was an unfamiliar sensation to Hare, and quite unnerving at first.

She continued to look up at Owl. He seemed so self-assured, so knowing. He seemed to want to help her, to guide her, but why would he do that, Hare asked herself. Why would he do that? The only answer she could give herself was the same reason that she always tried to help any animal in need: compassion.

A love of life, and a respect for all the woodland

 animals, even if they didn't treat Hare with the same respect. Hare thought back to the time Weasel had his paw caught in a trap and was crying out in pain. Thinking nothing for her own safety, Hare had immediately gone to his rescue.

The trap was very stiff and heavy, but after much heaving and shoving, Hare had been able to release Weasel's paw and collapsed backwards onto the embankment. She'd looked at the sky, then lifted her head slightly, smiling, as Weasel towered over her, silhouetted against the sky with the sun behind him. His fear had turned into anger, and Hare thought that was a perfectly reasonable reaction, until it seemed that he was blaming her for him being trapped, rather than thanking her for helping set him free. His rage was growing as Hare decided just to listen before she said her piece, but instead of hearing that, Weasel had bitten Hare's side and run off. She had never seen him again but often went over the incident in her head to justify Weasel's behaviour.

She remembered the time when Rat had been cornered by a gang of crows, wanting her to give up the scraps of food she'd found and was taking home to her babies. She would not have been able to take on all the crows singlehandedly, so Hare had dropped her own lunch to go and side with Rat against the bully birds. The bigger of them had jumped in  and grabbed Rat's morsels, launching into the air just as Hare arrived, so she shouted after him and the others who flew off, cackling, after him.

When Hare turned back round, she saw Rat scampering off in the other direction, with Hare's lunch tucked under her arm. Hare had felt cheated and betrayed, especially as she would gladly have given her small rations to Rat for her babies if Rat had only stayed around long enough. Instead, Rat had destroyed Hare's trust, and that incident was still impacting her today.

Looking up at Owl, Hare longed for him to say something soothing, something that would help comfort her and go some way to convincing her that leaving Fox and her old self behind was the

right thing to do. She was not sure that she could believe him, but she wanted the chance to try. Owl's voice was gentle and to begin with she could still hear Snake and Fox's words above his voice telling her that she was wrong.

"Do not be fooled, Hare, into believing the greatest mistruth in all of the countryside," Owl said, looking out into the distance.

"What's that?" Hare asked, almost not sure what to believe any more.

"We are led to believe that there comes a point in all our lives when everything that happens to us is down to fate. That is simply not true. We are always in control of our own lives, and we alone make the decisions."

Owl flew off into the distance leaving Hare alone with her thoughts. Hopping along slowly, absentmindedly, she considered what he had just said. Could that be true? Maybe it was time to change the narrative in her head and give herself a voice.

Hare became aware that the day was drawing to a close and the sun was sinking beyond the hills of the horizon. It was time to find somewhere safe to spend the night. Hare would rest her body but suspected that her mind would continue at pace throughout the dark hours. In her heart, Hare knew she couldn't sustain this 'always on' state forever but her head was strong and insisted, promising it wouldn't continue without end, just never confirming what the scenario for relaxing would be. They weren't there yet.

Hare found a secluded hollow under a hawthorn that would suit her for the night. It was homely if not home, but home hadn't been a haven for some time now and in many ways, it was a positive to have left.

Dusk passed and the darkness enveloped everything Hare could see and feel, which led her racing mind to taunt her more. What if everything in life would be black for Hare now? What if she'd made a terrible mistake, and all this darkness was how Mother Nature was letting her know? It felt as if another shadow crept over her thoughts and blacked out the recent successes and perceived positive steps.

Soon after Hare had shuffled into the hollow and flattened her ears along her back to rest, the moon appeared from behind the clouds and showered the landscape in beautiful silver light. It was breath-taking. She scrunched her eyes up trying to shut out the light and focus instead on rest and sleep.

Suddenly, as if she'd heard the sound of a farmer's shotgun, Hare was sitting upright, wide awake. Her restless mind had served her something of an epiphany; this moonlight might truly be the antidote to the darkness. She'd been happy enough to believe the symbolism of the black clouds and shadows, so why not take the next step now that the darkness had been vanquished? Hare bounced out from under the bush, enjoying the movement of her dancing shadows on the ground and thought about what this might mean. She ran, and jumped, laughing all the while at the thought that perhaps this really was a turning point for her. Not caring where she was going, just happy to be feeling free and on the cusp of something huge, Hare followed a tractor track through a field. Off to her right, she spotted a pond and hesitated briefly before approaching the water carefully, placing her paws precisely as she reached the end of the bank. Gingerly, Hare peered over the edge. The water was so still, with not a breath of air, and the moonlight highlighted her reflection. She looked different somehow. Perhaps she was imagining it. She looked again. Something had definitely changed. She looked around, expecting one of the animals to sidle up and tell her not to be so silly, to put these daft ideas out of her head, to stop this crazy talk. But there was no-one there. No Snake. No Fox. No Weasel or Rat, nor any of the other animals that Hare realised she was trying to move on from.

"I can do this," she whispered to no-one in particular, "Why not me?"

Making her way back to the hawthorn bush, Hare felt excitement brewing for everything that lay ahead of her. It wouldn't be easy, she knew that. Sometimes, making the decision to try is the easy bit and the hardest parts lie ahead.

But she knew she was ready to try something, ready to make a plan to do whatever she wanted, with the belief that she could make it happen. And with renewed determination and head and heart finally beginning to work together, Hare was able to sleep long and deep, waking at dawn to start the next chapter.

Hare felt the adventure was coming. She didn't know what it looked like yet, or when it would appear, but she felt confident that it would show itself sooner or later and she'd know it when she saw it. Until then, she was content to go about her business, keeping her head down so as not to draw attention to herself, waiting.

Hare busied herself helping out the other animals, picking fruit, looking after mischievous kittens and leverets, happy not to rush things.

One day, when Hare had almost forgotten she was waiting for a sign, her whiskers twitched. She sniffed the air. Unfamiliar. She sniffed again, deeper this time. Smoke. Smoke! Hare's eyes widened in panic as time stood still and she felt rooted to the spot. A cry from Mouse snapped her out of her freeze and she turned in the direction of the wail. Mouse was scurrying around her pups, frantically trying to see who was missing as the flames marched towards her nest. The babies did not understand the severity of the situation and carrying them all to safety was too much for Mouse on her own. Thinking nothing of her own position, Hare ran to help Mouse and her pups, against the flow of the other animals hurrying to save themselves.

When Hare would look back on this moment, she would be able to explain what happened in some detail, but not how. It was pure instinct, and that drove her determination. When she reached Mouse, she had made her focus and think. How many pups were there, who was missing, where had she last seen them? No mouse would be left behind. She rounded everyone up and guided them steadily in the direction others had run before, a route which was now clearly defined by trampled grass and pawprints on the ground.

When Mouse recalls the rescue, she firmly believes that without Hare, she and her babies would have perished. It was a moment she will never forget, knowing that there was someone willing to help, in the most challenging and dangerous of circumstances, and that she had not been forgotten.

For now, the adrenaline pumped through their fragile bodies as they sought sanctuary from the encroaching heat, flames licking the air and swallowing the field behind them. The pawprints they had been following stopped at the river. Hare took a deep breath and swallowed, composing herself for the next step as she took in the wide expanse of water in front of her. She knew she could swim, although she wasn't confident in the water. But what about the little mice? Could they hold their own against the current? There was no time to think further. Hare's eyes darted about the scene in front of her and came to rest on a fallen branch, trapped against a rock by the moving water. She might just be able to reach it.

Surprised by her own strength, Hare was able to power herself from one boulder to another to reach the wood, staying out of the water. But now the moment had come; she would need to swim back with her make-shift raft because it was too big to carry. It would hold Mouse and her family and keep them dry, and if the plan worked, the power in Hare's hind legs would see them across the river to refuge on the far bank.

Hare hoped it would work. It had to. Not working just wasn't an option. Hare was able to call on a determination deep within her as she took another deep breath and jumped into the water.

As she splashed, she felt a sharp pain in her paw that travelled like a shock up her leg. She didn't have time to investigate what had been lurking beneath the water, just knew that it had hurt. Trying to ignore the pain pulsing through her paw, she focused on the little mice on the riverbank and began to swim.

Mouse began to cheer encouragement, and the pups joined in as loudly as they could. Their

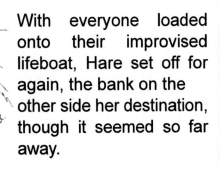

squeaks carried over the water and helped Hare find an extra gear.

With everyone loaded onto their improvised lifeboat, Hare set off for again, the bank on the other side her destination, though it seemed so far away.

"Focus," Hare told herself, "Breathe," and she swam like her life depended on it, because it did. Her life, and the fate of the mouse family, was down to Hare now. The squeaky cheers continued and didn't let up. Mouse had been unable to speak until they reached the bank, and she was within jumping distance to hold the branch while her pups disembarked.

"I can't ever thank you enough," Mouse cried, through tears of relief. Hare counted the little mice off the boat substitute and stood to make her own way to shore. She stumbled on a loose stone and lost her footing, slipping back into the water. Unable to regain her balance, the river took her and washed her downstream. Hare, startled and frightened of the unknown, knew this force was not something she could counter. She would just go with it. There was no choice, and that realisation gave Hare some peace.

She thought of Owl, and of some of the things he had said to her. When he'd mentioned falling into water, she was sure he hadn't intended it as prophecy though nevertheless Hare remembered that she wouldn't drown as long as she held her head high, out of the river. She was able to keep her head above the water, so there was no immediate danger for her and instead she would concentrate on what would happen next.

Her trust was repaid and soon the pace of the water began to slow, and the river became much shallower. Her paw still aching, she reached another down to test the depth and was delighted to realise she could stand once more, and she began wading to the edge.

As she hauled herself onto the riverbank, exhausted but finally safe, Hare closed her eyes and allowed her other senses to take over. Sometimes, it's not just your eyes that allow clarity of vision. She listened to the reeds blowing in the breeze, and while she couldn't hear the river, her nose knew it was there. A gust of wind sent a chill racing down her body and her soggy coat offered little warmth.

She lay still, nevertheless, just taking the time to reflect. How lucky she was! How grateful she was knowing that others had also come through it. Hare pressed her paws into the muddy bank and felt the sensation between her pads. Is this what freedom felt like?

"You did it, Hare!" Owl called down to her. "You made it! You should be so proud of yourself."

"I am," thought Hare. Proud because she had got herself and so many others to safety, proud

because she'd achieved a physical feat she would not have expected herself capable of not so long ago, and proud because of the challenges she'd overcome.

Hare was also surprised that Owl was allowing himself to be so candid. There was emotion, warmth and compassion. Right there!

Things Hare had searched for so long, and now, just as she'd stopped looking and had diverted her focus to fleeing the immediate danger, she had found them. Or rather, they had found her. What if they had been there all along? Hare wondered if perhaps she'd been looking in the wrong place.

Something had changed for Hare, and she couldn't quite determine what that was. Had the river trip somehow strengthened her bond with Owl?
Maybe it was the connection to herself that was driving this new sense of achievement and purpose.

Hare raised her head and looked around.
Smiling to herself, with a mixture of relief,
happiness and clarity, "Yes," she thought, "This is
it. You'll know when you get there."

From

"I will not let anyone walk through my mind with their dirty feet" - **Mahatma Gandhi**

To

"You are only as free as the choices you make" – **Lorraine Stamp**

<u>Hare Invites you to now reflect</u>

Thank you for taking the time to read
Hare's Journey of a Thousand Miles.
I hope you enjoyed it as much as I enjoyed putting
it all together and sharing it.

I now would like you to enjoy this part of the book
as a journal reflection, as a guide on your own
journey to raise awareness and reflect on your
own life. It is my intention that by sharing some
of the characters I have experienced along the
way, you will be able to recognise your own, and
to know if they are people who will help you thrive.

A question that so many people ask is, where do I start? It is a great question, however getting started is the best thing to do. Begin by spending just five minutes every day jotting down your thoughts in answer to these questions. You will soon get into the flow, allowing yourself longer to think and write, and you will start to find some of the answers appearing in your mind as you begin to relax and get in the zone.

Habits are formed by taking action, not just thinking about it.

The following questions are there to prompt thought. You can always just grab some paper and free write your own thoughts based on what you have read.

As you were reading *Hare's Journey of a Thousand Miles* could you feel a connection to any of the characters?

On the following pages, I invite you to spend some time reflecting on some questions about your life and if you relate to any of these characters in the book.

<u>Let's get started</u>

How did you feel whilst you were reading the story?

What emotions did you experience?

What thoughts did you have?

Can you recall parts of the story that you felt
more connected to and why?

Throughout our lives we get to meet many people. Some of these people are around us for a lifetime, some for fairly long periods of time and others for not that long at all. We may start to notice that some of those people truly lift us up and some know how to pull us down.

Let's look at some of the characters that Hare met on the journey

Snake

Can you relate to snake in any way?

Snake

Is there a snake character currently around you? Or have you experienced a snake in your life?

Snake

How do you feel when there is snake around you?

Snake

Are they there to support, encourage, empower you? Or is there a possibility that you feel restricted?

Snake

Can you imagine what your life would look and feel like with no snakes around you?

Fox

Can you connect with the Fox character?

Fox

Is there anyone around you that is possibly like Fox?

Fox

When you are around someone like Fox how do you feel?

Fox

What would your life look and feel like if Fox was not around you?

Fox

Having Fox in your life, what costs are you currently paying?

Fox

What's the consequence of keeping Fox in your life?

Fox

Is there any part of Fox that maybe you relate to within yourself?

Rat

Can you connect with the rat character?

Rat

Is rat adding value to your life?

Rat

How do you feel when rat is with you?

Rat

Can you imagine what your life would look and feel like without rat as part of it?

Rat

Can you recognise other rat characters around you?

Weasel

Can you connect with the weasel character?

Weasel

Do you feel that there is a weasel in your life?

Weasel

Does Weasel add value to your life?

Weasel

How do you feel when Weasel is around you?

Weasel

Can you imagine what your life would look and feel like without Weasel as part of it?

Weasel

Can you recognise other weasel
characters around you?

Owl

Can you connect with the owl character?

Owl

Do you feel that there is an Owl in your life?

Owl

Does Owl add value to your life?

Owl

How do you feel when Owl is around you?

Owl

Can you imagine what your life would look and feel like without owl?

Owl

Can you recognise other owl characters around you?

Mouse

Can you connect with the mouse character?

Mouse

Do you feel that there is a Mouse in your life?

Mouse

Does Mouse add value to your life?

Mouse

How do you feel when Mouse is around you?

Mouse
Can you imagine what your life would look and feel like without Mouse?

Mouse

Can you recognise other characters around you like Mouse?

Other characters you may have met

What other woodland characters would be on your life journey?

Other characters you may have met

Name of character?

Other characters you may have met

How do you feel when they are around you?

Other characters you may have met

How can you bring more characters into your life that you feel add value/meaning/purpose/peace/happiness into your life?

Other characters you may have met

If you were to take one step today after reflecting on the story and characters that would really help you to become healthier and happier, what would that step be?

Other characters you may have met

What difference would that one step create for you?

Other characters you may have met

And what would a bigger step look like?

Other characters you may have met

And how would that make you feel?

Other characters you may have met

What do you really want for you in this lifetime?

Your environment

If you were to describe your environment around, you. What words would you use to describe it?

Your environment

How does your environment make you feel?

Your environment

If you could describe your ideal environment, what would it look like?

Your environment

Does your current environment allow you to be yourself, that authentic version of you?

Your environment

If you were to look around your environment, do you feel it relates to the person you are today?

Your environment

How do you feel about the things that you have within your environment? If you were to walk around your environment, would you say that you experience pleasant emotions?

Your environment

How could you make changes to your environment to increase those pleasant emotions?

Now let's take a look at Hare

I want you to imagine that you are Hare just for a moment.

As you think of yourself as Hare in this story, what thoughts and emotions are arising?

Now let's take a look at Hare

What would you do differently as Hare went on this journey?

Now let's take a look at Hare

If you had the opportunity now to rewrite Hare's story from the beginning, what would it look and feel like? What characters would you like to meet and spend more time with?

Have a go at rewriting the story in your own words about Hare's journey of a thousand miles and tag #rewriteharesjourney

You might get a mention in the next book released *Hare's Journey of a Thousand Smiles*

#rewriteharesjourney

#rewriteharesjourney

#rewriteharesjourney

#rewriteharesjourney

#rewriteharesjourney

#rewriteharesjourney

Well done on getting this far in the book. How do you feel? Did it feel like a workout?

A bit like exercising for our physical health, it is so important we give our minds a good workout too. Sometimes, our way of thinking, our experiences and our knowledge can be the biggest hindrance for living a more fulfilling life. Remember you are in control of all those conscious choices every second, every minute and every hour of every day. Make the right choices for your happier and healthier life ahead.

When we can look back at the choices we have made, and the lessons we have learnt along the way, we become even more resilient for the path ahead.

If you had to think of one word right now of how you want to feel on most days, what would that be?

If you had to think of one word right now of how you want to feel on most days, what would that be?

Know that this is possible. If Hare can do it, so can you.

Be gentle and kind with yourself, and take one step at a time.

Love Hare

Lorraine Stamp is an award-winning international keynote speaker and a positive psychology wellness coach, on a mission to help 3 million people transform their lives through her mindset and transformational coaching programmes and retreats.

She is so proud to be speaking all over the world to spread sprinkles of happiness everywhere she goes.

Lorraine helps organisations, teams, and individuals in creating happiness and wellbeing by using positive psychology and neuroscience to cultivate a wellbeing focus in lives and businesses.

Lorraine felt that her most treasured gift in life had to be shared and she identified several characters that she encountered on her life journey so far to tell this story. During the launch of one of her Personal Transformation Quest programmes she was blessed to have met writer, Rowen Campbell. They spent nearly two year's working together to download Lorraine's personal story with Rowen translating it into this incredible story,

Hare's Journey of a Thousand Miles.

Lorraine found the whole experience very emotional as she re-told her lived experiences, but then realised how cathartic the whole process was.

Lorraine has worked with thousands of people to date, helping them understand what might be currently holding them back or resisting change, and helping empower them to rebuild their confidence to achieve a much happier and healthier life.

You can find out more about the work Lorraine is doing at www.youllknowwhenyougetthere.co.uk

Lorraine is also running her coaching programmes online and at her retreats - please visit her website for more information. She would love your feedback on her book, so please do share your reviews and post on social media using #haresjourney

Rowen Campbell is a copy and content writer, marketing manager and mum of two.

She loves to tell a story and when she's not writing, you'll find her outside on an adventure, or curled up somewhere with a good book. She is currently writing her first novel.

To find out more about Rowen pop over to www.rowencampbell.com or email her at rowenwrites@gmail.com